Nuclear Waste Disposal

Can We Rely on Bedrock?

Other titles of interest

BERGMAN	*Subsurface Space* (3-volume set)
BROWN	*Rock Characterization: Testing and Monitoring*
DE VOLPI	*Proliferation, Plutonium and Policy*
FRITZ	*Future Energy Consumption of the Third World*
GABOR	*Beyond the Age of Waste*, 2nd edition
GARDEL	*Energy: Economy and Prospective* (French language edition also available)
GRENON	*The Nuclear Apple and the Solar Orange*
McVEIGH	*Sun Power*, 2nd edition
ROSS	*Energy from the Waves*, 2nd edition
SECRETARIAT FOR FUTURES STUDIES	*Resources, Society and the Future*
SECRETARIAT FOR FUTURES STUDIES	*Solar versus Nuclear: Choosing Energy Futures*
SIMEONS	*Hydro-power*
WILLIAMS	*Hydrogen Power*
WILLIAMS	*Nuclear Non-proliferation*

Pergamon related journals — *Free specimen copy gladly sent on request*

ADVANCES IN TUNNELLING TECHNOLOGY AND SUBSURFACE USE
GEOFORUM
JOURNAL OF STRUCTURAL GEOLOGY
INTERNATIONAL JOURNAL OF ROCK MECHANICS AND MINING SCIENCES & GEOMECHANICS ABSTRACTS
NUCLEAR AND CHEMICAL WASTE MANAGEMENT
UNDERGROUND SPACE

Nuclear Waste Disposal

Can We Rely on Bedrock?

By

ULF LINDBLOM, DEng

Hagconsult ab, Göteborg, Sweden

and

PAUL GNIRK, PhD

RE/SPEC Inc., Rapid City, South Dakota, USA

PERGAMON PRESS

OXFORD NEW YORK TORONTO SYDNEY PARIS FRANKFURT

U.K.	Pergamon Press Ltd., Headington Hill Hall, Oxford OX3 0BW, England
U.S.A.	Pergamon Press Inc., Maxwell House, Fairview Park, Elmsford, New York 10523, U.S.A.
CANADA	Pergamon Press Canada Ltd., Suite 104 150 Consumers Road, Willowdale, Ontario M2J 1P9, Canada
AUSTRALIA	Pergamon Press (Aust.) Pty. Ltd., P.O. Box 544, Potts Point, N.S.W. 2011, Australia
FRANCE	Pergamon Press SARL, 24 rue des Ecoles, 75240 Paris, Cedex 05, France
FEDERAL REPUBLIC OF GERMANY	Pergamon Press GmbH, 6242 Kronberg-Taunus, Hammerweg 6, Federal Republic of Germany

First Edition 1982

British Library Cataloguing in Publication Data
Library of Congress Catolog Card no.:

Lindblom, Ulf
  Nuclear waste disposal.
  1. Radioactive waste disposal
  I. Title   II. Gnirk, Paul
  621.48'38   TD812

  ISBN 0-08-027608-3 Hardcover
  ISBN 0-08-027595-8 Flexicover

Printed in Great Britain by A. Wheaton & Co. Ltd., Exeter.

Foreword

We know that nuclear power reactors produce useful energy in the form of electricity and heat. We also know that they produce waste materials from the nuclear reaction. These are dangerous to mankind for time periods of thousands of years into the future. The nations of the world now using nuclear power are faced with one of the most difficult problems of modern times: *How is it possible to isolate safely the nuclear wastes from all living organisms for such long periods of time?* Regardless of the future of nuclear energy in the world, this question *must* be answered in an acceptable and reasonable manner to both the public and technical communities of our civilization. We must be confident that our children and their descendants will not be unexpectedly exposed to the dangers of nuclear wastes that were produced in our generation.

A solution, which has been suggested in such countries as the United States, Canada, Sweden, and the Federal Republic of Germany, is to deposit canisters of nuclear waste in tunnels and rooms in deep rock formations, say at depths of 500-1100 m (1600-3600 ft). Such an underground facility in a large body of rock is known as a *repository*. The tunnels and rooms are excavated by mining techniques and the waste canisters placed in vertical drillholes in the floor. Some years after all the canisters have been emplaced, the repository will be backfilled and sealed. This concept is know as Mined Geological Disposal of Nuclear Wastes. *Will this method of waste disposal provide the isolation necessary to safely protect future generations of mankind?*

The main emphasis when selecting a repository site is placed on the past history of geologic stability of a region. Although the repository itself may occupy only perhaps 2 or 3 km^2 (about 1 mi^2) of underground space, the geologic region could cover some 250,000 km^2 (about 100,000 mi^2) of land area. Geologic stability means that the rock formations have been relatively quiet for hundreds of thousands of years or longer. This is to say that there is little evidence of earthquake damage or violent and extensive fracturing of the rocks. In addition, areas of mineralization with ore-bearing rocks, such as iron and copper deposits, are avoided since future generations may mine these areas for the needs of their society. *Is it possible to find a rock formation for a repository which will not experience an earthquake or be disturbed by humans over the next tens of thousands of years? If indeed we assume that the repository may be disrupted or breached by some natural or human-induced event, what will be the consequences to mankind if the waste canisters are damaged?*

Evaluation of geologic regions for repository sites has been in progress in the United States and the Federal Republic of Germany since the early 1970s with initial emphasis placed on salt. Subsequently in the United States, the program was broadened to include a greater variety of rock types, including basalt, granite, shale, and tuff. During the late 1970s, the programs in Canada and Sweden began the search for repository sites in large masses of granitic rock. Except for salt, most of these rock formations generally contain complex systems of joints and fractures, sometimes in great abundance and sometimes not. These systems are due partly to the process of geologic birth of the rock formation, and partly to the influence of forces in the earth's crust. Circulating water, albeit extremely slowly and at great depth, exists in the joints and fractures. Although the sedimentary rock formations containing bodies of salt may have relatively few joints and fractures, they do have systems of connected pores, or small voids, which are filled with circulating water. The salt formations themselves contain only minute quantities of water which do not circulate. It is the groundwater that will transport nuclear wastes to the surface if the repository and its waste canisters are damaged by an earthquake, or if the metal walls of the canisters corrode and expose the wastes to leaching by the groundwater. *Is it possible to predict the circulation patterns of groundwater around and through a repository over the next tens of thousands of years? Similarly, is it possible to predict accurately the time necessary for the circulating water to reach the ground surface? If so, is it possible to predict the concentrations of radioactive particles in the water when it reaches the ground surface?*

The format and contents of this book are based on those of a previous book, written by the senior author in Swedish and titled *Kan vi lita på urberget?* Now, however, a broader range of information is presented. The authors would like to thank Mr. Robert Källgren of Göteborg, Sweden, for his thoughtful preparation of the descriptive and informative illustrations; and Mr. Terje Brandshaug of RE/SPEC Inc. in Rapid City, SD/USA, for his careful translation of the original text from Swedish to English.*

January, 1981

ULF E. LINDBLOM
Göteborg, Sweden
and
PAUL F. GNIRK
Rapid City, SD/USA

Contents

The Form and Final Disposal of Nuclear Wastes

The Problem

Nuclear power plants produce electricity and heat, which are useful forms of energy to mankind. During production of this energy, the composition of the uranium fuel changes. The content of heavy elements and left-over fission products increases with time. Some of these elements and products will remain dangerously radioactive for hundreds and thousands of years. After some operating period, the ability of the uranium fuel to produce heat for driving the steam turbines for generation of electricity is diminished. It must then be removed from the reactor. This "spent fuel" is placed in water pools for cooling and storage. The problem, therefore, is what to do with this spent fuel, or nuclear waste, during future decades. The waste must be disposed of in a manner in which future generations of our descendants will be safely protected from its dangerous effects. It is extremely important to realize that we are faced with this problem regardless of the future of nuclear energy in the world. The disposal problem will simply not vanish if all nuclear reactors are shut down.

History tells us that civilizations and their organized governments may last for only a decade or so, or perhaps as long as several hundreds of years. These spans of time are only fractions of the life spans of some components of the nuclear waste. However, these components, or radionuclides, do possess a characteristic known as "half-life". That is, the radiation danger from a radionuclide will decrease by 50% over a given period of time. For example, iodine-129 has a half-life of 16 million years, while cesium-137 has a half-life of only 30 years. Generally speaking, the percentage of radionuclides with the relatively long half-lives in the nuclear waste is small as compared to the total volume. It is imperative that all the radionuclides must be disposed of in a manner that will not permit ingestation of dangerous quantities by living organisms.

During the past decade, the United States, Canada, Sweden, and the Federal Republic of Germany, as well as other countries with nuclear power reactors, have developed scientific and technical programs to deal with the problem of nuclear waste disposal. A number of solutions have been proposed. These include ejection into outer space, burial in the sediments underlying deep oceans, and burial in deep rock formations in the earth's crust. For many practical and scientific reasons, the last method has received the most attention. The concept is to bury metal containers of nuclear wastes in rooms and tunnels excavated by mining techniques in deep underground bodies of rock. After burial, the rooms, tunnels, and shafts to the ground surface would be backfilled and sealed. This method is commonly known as Mined Geologic Disposal of Nuclear Wastes. The intention is to let the rock isolate the harmful effects of the wastes from living organisms for hundreds of thousands of years. We must seriously ask ourselves the question *Will this method for nuclear waste disposal provide the necessary safety to all future generations of mankind?* The principal way in which the buried waste could be transported to the ground surface is by circulating groundwater. A discussion of the factors which could cause this situation to occur is the main theme of this book. We must mention now that leakage of radionuclides to the ground surface will not be a serious problem if the quantities are substantially less that those which already exist naturally in the water and food consumed by living organisms.

Fig. A. It is conceivable that radionuclides could be transported through the rock by the groundwater from the buried nuclear waste to the surface of the earth.

Fig. B. Furthermore, once the leakage occurs as shown in Fig. A, it is conceivable that the radionuclides would enter the drinking water and the irrigation water, and finally end up in the human body.

Will the rock protect us and our descendants from the harmful effects of the nuclear wastes?

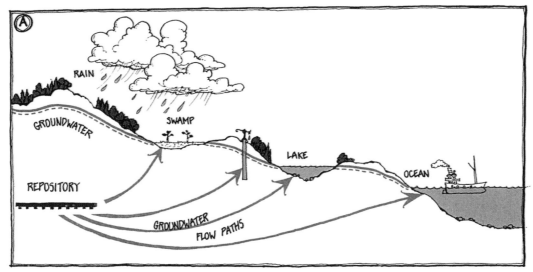

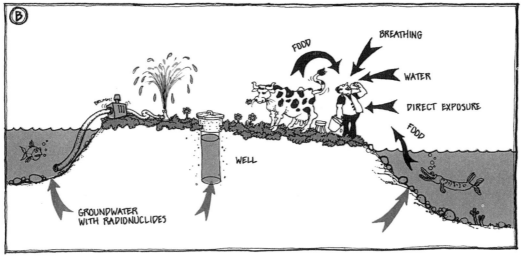

The Waste Form

The wastes from a nuclear power reactor include the spent fuel; dry trash from receiving, maintenance, and janitorial operations; resins from filtration and demineralization operations; filter cartridges from water clean-up systems; and slurry products from evaporate operations. Of these wastes, we are principally concerned in this book with the spent fuel, as it is both highly radioactive and heat generating.

Fig. A. The nuclear fuel cycle is a system of facilities and operations for the preparation, use, and disposal of the reactor fuel. At the "front-end" of the cycle, the uranium must be mined and milled to obtain what was called in the past "yellowcake". This is followed by enrichment of the uranium and fabrication of fuel rods for the reactor. After the fuel has been used in the nuclear reactor, the "spent fuel" is removed and placed in water pools for cooling and temporary storage. At this point, we are at the "back-end" of the cycle, and a decision must be made concerning final disposal. The spent fuel can be disposed of in its present form, that is as bundles of spent fuel rods. On the other hand, the spent fuel can be "reprocessed" to separate about 98% of the uranium and plutonium from the dangerous fission products and heavy metals. The uranium and plutonium will then be returned to the front-end of the cycle for use in the fabrication of the fuel rods, and the reprocessing wastes must be prepared for final disposal. Fig. B. If reprocessing of spent fuel is selected, then the reprocessing wastes will be "fixed" into a glass matrix, or perhaps a "synthetic" rock form. These forms exhibit very high resistances to leaching by water. In the first process, the wastes are melted together with materials, which form a homogenous glass substance (like color pigment melted with glass when a beer bottle is made).

Reprocessing techniques may vary, but approximately 9% of the glass matrix by weight will consist of reprocessing waste. It is proposed that the glass be encapsulated in a cylindrical container or canister of stainless steel, with a welded lid and perhaps a protective coating of titanium and lead. In Sweden, the canister will be approximately 1.8 m (6 ft) long by 61 cm (2 ft) in diameter. In the United States, the dimensions will be 3 m (10 ft) long by about 32 cm (13 in) in diameter. The amount of waste from every reactor will correspond to 3-4 m^3 of glass.

Fig. C. If reprocessing of spent fuel is not selected, then, in the Swedish concept, the fuel rods must first be separated from their metal jackets. The fuel rods will be placed in a thick-walled copper canister. The space between the rods will be filled with lead, and the canister closed with a copper lid. The canister will have a length of 4.7 m (15 ft) and a diameter of 77 cm (2.5 ft). In the reference disposal concept in the United States, a bundle of spent fuel rods will be placed in a carbon steel canister with a length of 4.7 m (15 ft) and a diameter of about 36 cm (14 in). Every reactor will produce 40-50 m^3 of waste per year including the waste containers.

The radiation danger and heat generation from the radionuclides with long half-lives in the nuclear wastes are substantially less than those with short half-lives for the first few hundreds of years. The heat is generated by decay of the radionuclides. The heat generation rates of the spent fuel and reprocessing wastes can be significantly reduced by cooling in water pools on the surface. In the United States it is planned to cool the spent fuel and reprocessing wastes at least 10 years before disposal. In Sweden, the cooling period would be 40 years.

NUCLEAR FUEL CYCLE

PROPOSED SWEDISH WASTE CANISTERS

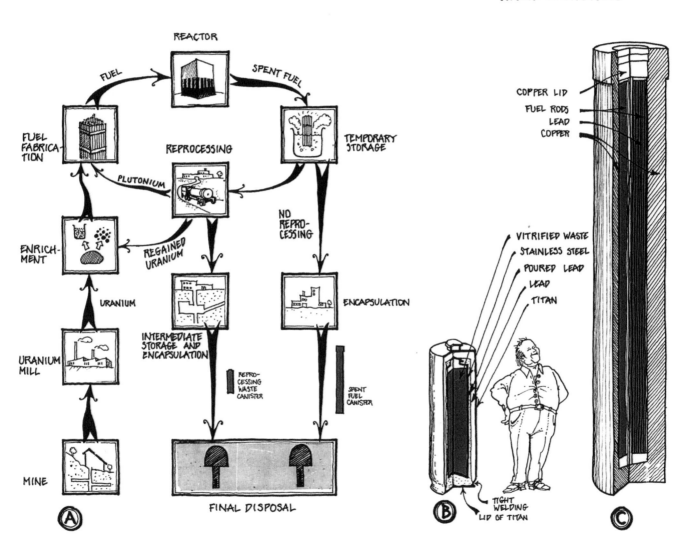

5

The Time Perspective

The safe disposal of nuclear wastes requires that predictions of the actions of mankind and nature must be made for periods of tens of thousands of years.

Looking backward in time, we know that radioactive rocks, forming the "natural nuclear reactors" at Oklo in Gabon began to operate at low power levels about 2 billion years ago. Located in rich deposits of uranium in sandstone, the fission reactions lasted for some 500,000 years and produced the equivalent of 100 billion kWh. The "nuclear wastes" have remained extremely localized in the surrounding rock to this day. Approximately 1.3 million years ago, major amounts of uranium and nickel were concentrated in the contact zone between sandstone and metamorphic rocks near Key Lake in northern Saskatchewan. It is thought that most of the lead produced by uranium and thorium decay since that time has migrated away from the deposit and into the overlying sandstone rock.

We know that the ancestors of today's people came to Europe some 200,000 years ago. They were responsible for the famous cave paintings of France and Spain. The last Ice Age began about 100,000 years ago, and ended approximately 10,000 years ago. The cultural development of mankind is contained entirely within the time period after the last Ice Age.

One can diagram the future on the same time scale as the past, and illustrate how the radioactivity of the nuclear wastes decays. In the figure, the danger from the nuclear waste is compared to the danger from uranium ore by using the "dilution method". The scale indicates the quantity of clean water required to dilute 1 g (approximately 0.04 oz) of spent fuel or corresponding amount of reprocessing waste, and still permit the water to be approved for drinking. For 1 g of freshly produced spent fuel, 50,000 m^3 (13 million gal) of clean water are necessary. By comparison, the volume of uranium ore needed to produce 1 g of reactor fuel has an inherent danger which requires dilution by 10 m^3 (2600 gal) of clean water.

From the figure we see that the spent fuel is more dangerous than the uranium ore for a very long time period, perhaps 10,000 years. However, after only several hundred years, the reprocessing waste is less dangerous than the uranium ore. The comparison takes into account the amounts of different radionuclides in the nuclear waste and the danger of these elements to the human body (the so-called relative danger). However, it does not consider the probability of exposure to these radionuclides and, if so, in what amounts.

The figure clearly illustrates the danger of nuclear waste disposal in a lake, for example. The consequences definitely would not be acceptable. The waste must be disposed of in a manner which gives us confidence that:

— any and all paths, by which the radionuclides could travel and eventually be consumed by living organisms, must be extremely long and contain many barriers;

— the quantities of radionuclides, which could travel to sources of drinking and irrigation water, must be extremely small, or highly diluted.

The disposal of nuclear wastes in mined rooms and tunnels in deep rock formations offers many advantages for achieving these goals, as well as some disadvantages.

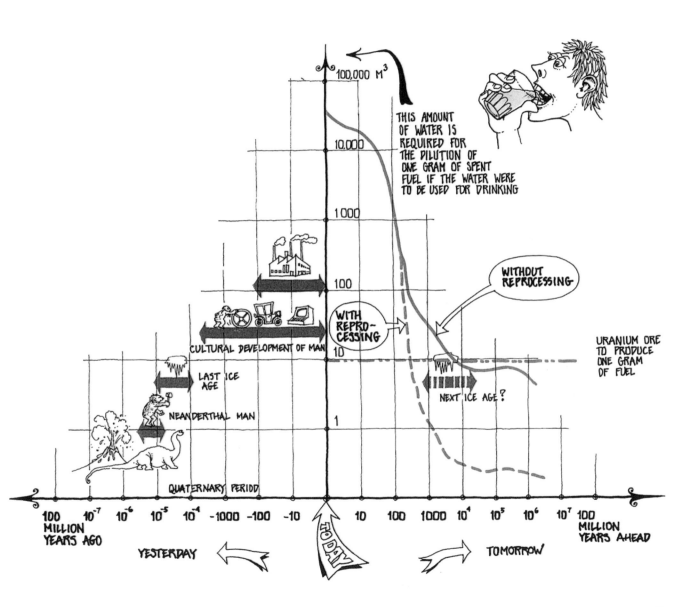

THIS AMOUNT OF WATER IS REQUIRED FOR THE DILUTION OF ONE GRAM OF SPENT FUEL IF THE WATER WERE TO BE USED FOR DRINKING

100,000 M³

10,000

1000

100

10

1

WITH REPROCESSING

WITHOUT REPROCESSING

URANIUM ORE TO PRODUCE ONE GRAM OF FUEL

CULTURAL DEVELOPMENT OF MAN

LAST ICE AGE

NEANDERTHAL MAN

NEXT ICE AGE?

QUATERNARY PERIOD

100 MILLION YEARS AGO 10^{-7} 10^{-6} 10^{-5} 10^{-4} -1000   -100   -10   10   100   1000 10^4 10^5 10^6 10^7 100 MILLION YEARS AHEAD

YESTERDAY

TODAY

TOMORROW

Mined Geological Disposal of Nuclear Waste

Mined geological disposal is a proposed method for burying waste canisters in deep rock formations. Tunnels, disposal rooms, and shafts to the surface will be excavated by mining techniques. Metal canisters of waste would be placed in drillholes in the floors of the disposal rooms. The depth and diameter of the drillhole would be considerably larger than the length and diameter of a waste canister. The extra space will be filled with a buffer or backfill material, such as bentonite or a mixture of bentonite and crushed rock. If future retrieval of the waste is a consideration, the drillhole may also be lined with a steel sleeve. This would simplify removal of a canister from its drillhole. After completing the emplacement of the waste canisters, the disposal room will be filled with crushed rock or a mixture of crushed rock and clay. Some time after all the disposal rooms have been used, the remaining tunnels and shafts to the surface will be filled and sealed. Natural earth materials, such as clays, crushed rock, and cement will be used as sealing materials. The ground surface above the buried waste will probably become a national park or monument, with a land area of perhaps 100 km² within which drilling activites would be forbidden. History tells us that civilizations with organized governments and precise records eventually disappear, or are absorbed into other civilizations. Therefore, we must assume that the burial site of the nuclear waste will finally be forgotten and the records lost.

Concerning the figure, the collection of disposal rooms, tunnels, and shafts to the surface is known as a "repository". The general layout is commonly similar for bedded salt, dome salt, granite, basalt, and other rock types, with some adjustment for rock structure. The repository depth may vary from rock type to rock type and from country to country. Generally, however, the depth will range somewhere between 500 and 1100 m (1600–3600 ft). The number of repositories and the waste-canister capacity of each depends on the projected needs of a particular country. In Sweden, for example, only one repository is planned in granite for a capacity of 9000 waste canisters, with disposal operations to begin in about the years 2020. The disposal area would be about 1.1 km² (280 acres), located at a depth of 500 m (1600 ft).

On the other hand, several repositories are currently being considered in the United States, with the first to become operational by the end of this century. The conceptual repository for a salt dome envisions a capacity of about 100,000 canisters of reprocessing wastes and approximately 500,000 drums of wastes with relatively low levels of radiation. This would require a repository with two disposal levels, with 186 disposal rooms for drums on the upper level and 580 rooms for canisters on the lower level. The lower level would need 485 km² (1200 acres) of area located at a depth of 600 m (2000 ft). The conceptual design for a repository in basalt visualizes a capacity of 35,000 spent fuel canisters and 32,000 low-level waste drums. A disposal area of 7.6 km² (1950 acres) on a single level would be required, located at a depth of 1130 m (3700 ft).

The dimensions of the disposal rooms vary according to the depth, rock type, expected heat load from the buried canisters, and the waste form. Since the spent-fuel canisters are longer than the reprocessing waste canisters, their emplacement will require comparatively greater room height. This could vary from 4 to 6 m (13–21 ft) and the width from 3.5 to 5.5 m (11–13 ft). The lengths of the rooms may range from 180 to 1100 m (550–3600 ft). The drillhole depths and diameters also vary with the waste form. For spent fuel, the depths may range from 6 to 8 m (21–26 ft) and the diameters from 1.2 to 1.5 m (4–5 ft). For reprocessing waste, the depth and diameter would be comparatively less.

The waste form, metal canister, and drillhole backfill (and the steel sleeve when used) are collectively known as the "waste package". Together with the surrounding rock, these materials form a system of multiple barriers for preventing the escape of radionuclides from the waste to the ground surface. Leaching of the radionuclides by groundwater in hard rock, or by brine in salt, will require hundreds and probably thousands of years. Before this can happen, the metal canister must be corroded and dissolved away. Depending on the type of metal, this corrosion process may require decades (mild steel) to hundreds of years (copper). The backfill material, probably clay or clay crushed rock mixture, will be dry when it is placed around the canister. As the clay becomes wet, it will swell and restrict water flow towards the metal canister. When the water eventually leaches the waste and circulates outward to the rock, some of the radionuclides will become attached to the clay particles. This is known as "retardation" of radionuclide migration by the process of "sorbtion". It has even been suggested that charcoal be added to the backfill material to improve its retardation capability. The final barrier is, of course, the rock itself. Much of the remainder of the book will discuss the characteristics of this barrier and its impact on radionuclide migration to the earth's surface.

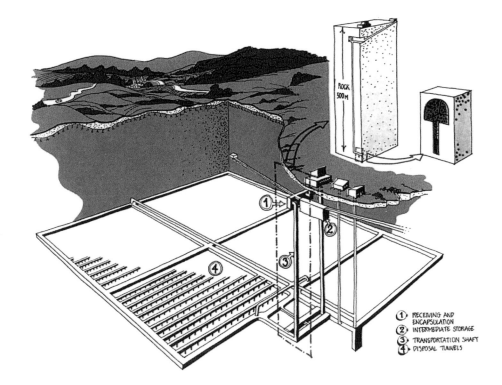

ROCK 500 M

1. RECEIVING AND ENCAPSULATION
2. INTERMEDIATE STORAGE
3. TRANSPORTATION SHAFT
4. DISPOSAL TUNNELS

Alternative Methods of Nuclear Waste Disposal

On the previous page we have described the method of mined geologic disposal of nuclear wastes. What about alternative methods? Yes, there are some, and we shall briefly discuss the more well-known ones now. There is one common drawback, however, to the use of any of these alternative methods. The drawback is perhaps partly physiological and partly technical. It is that these methods allow little if any opportunity for retrieval of the nuclear wastes at some future date. Why would anyone want to retrieve the nuclear wastes from a disposal area? Economic reasons perhaps, because the spent fuel does contain recoverable amounts of uranium and plutonium. Safety reasons possibly, because of unacceptable radionuclide leakage to the environment, or because of remarkable technical advances in safe disposal techniques in the future.

Fig. A. *Rock-melting disposal*. This method would involve placing hot liquid or solid wastes in mined cavities or drillholes in rock, at depths of perhaps 3 km (2 mi). The heat from the waste would melt the rock and allow the two materials to mix. The liquid mixture would eventually cool and solidify into a rock-waste mass. The final shape and consistency of the mass is uncertain, as is its resistance to leaching action by circulating groundwater.

Fig. B. *Sea-bed Disposal*. It has been proposed that waste canisters would be lowered into drillholes in layers of fine-grained sediments on the bottom of a deep ocean. Extreme care must be taken while handling and emplacing the canisters because an accident could harm marine life. However, radionuclides, leaking from damaged canisters, would be diluted in large amounts of water. Water can move only very slowly through the sediments, which appear to sorb radionuclides efficiently. The consequences of disturbing the canisters in the future by mineral mining on the ocean floor is uncertain.

Fig. C. *Ice sheet disposal*. There have been suggestions that nuclear wastes could be placed in thick ice sheets near the poles of the earth. The canisters would be lowered into shallow drillholes and either anchored with cables to the surface or permitted to sink downward to the bedrock by melting the ice. The safety of this method has many questions, as it depends on future climatic conditions and natural ice movements.

Fig. D. *Disposal in outer space*. Disposal of nuclear waste in outer space by rockets has been studied for some years. Because of the large volumes of wastes, this method is impractical at the current time, except perhaps for small concentrated quantities of the most dangerous radionuclides. The costs would be quite high. The consequences of an accident or malfunction during launching or staging in orbit are probably unacceptable at this time.

As a related matter to the disposal question, people often ask why the heat from the nuclear wastes cannot be used for beneficial means. The answer involves principally economics and safety. Due to the required spacing between bundles of fuel rods stored in a water pool, the circulating water is not heated to very high temperatures. This "low-grade" heat would have to be transferred to a separate water or air system by a heat exchanger. Finally, the heat would have to be distributed by some method to homes, schools, large buildings, and manufacturing plants, which are generally not located immediately adjacent to a nuclear power plant. Considering the costs of the heat exchanger-distribution system and the safety measures required by public concerns, such a proposition would be uneconomical.

It would be unwise for us to suggest that mined geologic disposal and the methods discussed above are the absolute best that mankind can devise. Technical advancements in general over the past 100 years have greatly exceeded the wildest expectations and imaginations of the world's best scientific minds of 1880. Solution of the nuclear waste disposal problem requires the concentrated and coordinated efforts of our most talented people. For both practical and scientific reasons, a reasonable disposal method must be selected now and studied in great detail before actual use. This is the situation with mined geologic disposal. Remember that the first waste canister will not be placed for permanent disposal in a rock formation for perhaps 20 years or more. Based on multitudes of technology advancements during the last two decades, one should optimistically expect substantial refinements in nuclear waste disposal technology.

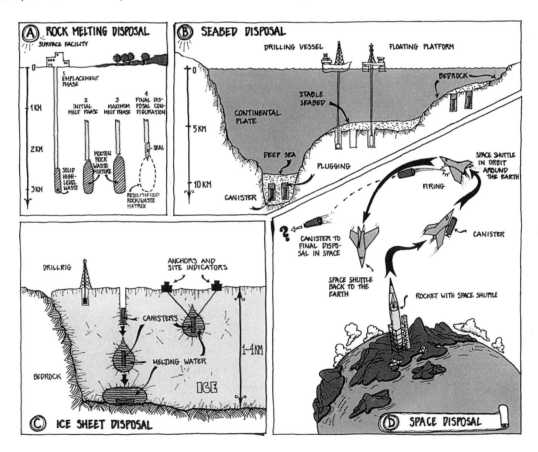

The Natural Rock and Groundwater

The Structure of Hard Rock

Throughout this book, the term "hard rock" is used for collectively classifying such rocks as granite, basalt, and tuff. These rocks contain natural fractures and systems of joints. Sedimentary rocks, such as sandstone and limestone, generally contain connected voids or pores, but comparatively few fractures and joints. Shales have both pores, but poorly connected, and fractures. This is also the case with tuff.

All of the rocks named above do have pores. In granite, for example, the natural fractures and joints are the main conduits for water flow, as the pores are usually small and not well connected.

Fig. A. The continents consist of shields, platforms, and mountain ranges. The shields are areas that contain the oldest rocks on earth. They were formed when hot melted rock moved upward from inside the earth and through the crustal rocks, some one billion or more years ago. For the most part, these areas have been stable for more than a billion years, since the formation of the mountain ranges. The platform areas were once the floors of oceans which moved upward over geologic time. They consist of layers of sedimentary rocks, formed by deposition of sediments. These were carried by water from the shield areas into the oceans. The mountain ranges were formed last by movements of the earth's crust. They surround the shields and platforms.

The rocks in the shield area have been exposed to different loadings over geologic time. These loadings have come from both below and above the earth's surface. The loadings from below have come from movements of the continents as they drift like gigantic floating plates, but ever so slowly. The loadings from above were due to the glaciers. The last Ice Age began some 100,000 years ago

and ended about 10,000 years ago. The weight of the ice caused the rock to sink. When the ice melted, the rock began to rise, or rebound slowly like a great coil spring. In northern Scandinavia, for example, the ground is still rising at the rate of about 1 cm (0.4 in) per year.

Fig. B. The loadings of past geologic time have created faults, fractures, and joints, and crushed zones in the rock.

The joints are really regular systems of fracture planes, with preferred directions in different areas. However, there has been no visible movement of one wall of the joint with respect to the other. The crushed zones are localized regions in the rock in which fractures and joints are highly abundant. They are "zones of weakness" in the earth's crust, and were carved into valleys by the glaciers. These zones also erode more easily than the huge "blocks" of rock in between.

From a distance, a cross-section of the rock mass would look like a mosaic, with large zones of relatively solid rock bordered by fractured zones. Commonly, the fracturing becomes less severe with increasing depth. There are fewer joints, and the zones of weakness become less apparent. Near the surface, the many fractures and joints permit the surface water to flow into the rock, which acts as a reservoir. However, after only a few tens of meters of depth, the capacity of this reservoir becomes smaller. This is part of the reason why it is difficult to find a good water well in granitic rocks unless you are fortunate enough to drill into a crushed zone.

Fig. C. Basalt was formed when hot lava was forced upward from inside the earth through fissures or large fractures in the crust, and spilled out as flat sheets onto the surface. These eruptions occurred during various periods in later geologic time, and caused individual layers of basalt to be formed on top of each other. The bottom of a flow is generally fine-grained or glassy. On the other hand, the top is commonly irregular and contains small voids caused by rising bubbles of air or gas in the molten lava as it cooled. Lava ejected under or into bodies of water forms a structure that resembles a pile of pillows. Joints may occur in the flows, but they resemble columns with five or six sides.

In passing, we mention that welded tuff is formed when very hot solid particles from volcanic eruptions settle onto the surface and "weld" together.

Fig. D. The basalt flows in the northwestern United States were formed by volcanoes, which erupted enormous quantities of basaltic lava over very large areas. These eruptions took place for long time periods between 9 and 15 million years ago. In some areas, the total depth of the individual flows ranges from 2700 to 4900 m (9000–16000 ft).

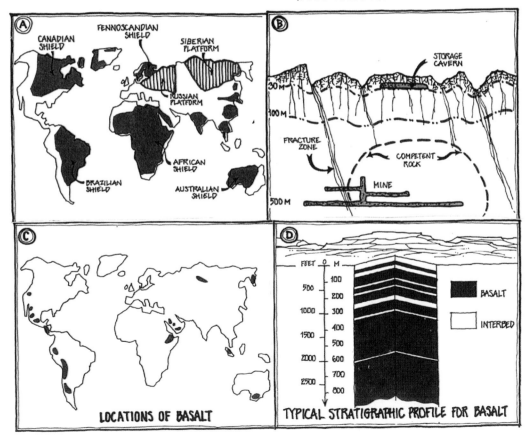

LOCATIONS OF BASALT

TYPICAL STRATIGRAPHIC PROFILE FOR BASALT

15

The Structure of Salt Formations

Massive salt beds are formed in layers above sedimentary rocks by evaporation of lake waters in arid regions, or in lagoons near the ocean. Because of cyclic changes in the climate from humid to dry over geologic time, the salt beds may be interbedded with layers of shale, limestone, and other sedimentary rocks. Salt formed in land-locked basins will have a composition which reflects the chemical nature of the surrounding rocks. It may contain useful amounts of gypsum and potash which may be mined economically. On the other hand, salt formed in lagoons may have a high content of pure salt.

Fig. A. Massive deposits of salt occur down the middle of North America, with others located on the southeastern edge of the Great Lakes and the eastern edge of Canada. These formations have probably been formed by evaporation from lakes in land-locked basins. Many of these formations have thick beds, tens to hundreds of meters thick, which are relatively flat lying. Other formations are tilted, or have been warped like folds in a blanket by movements within the continental mass. In some regions, the tops of the beds are being dissolved away by circulating groundwater in the overlying sedimentary rocks. This has resulted in collapse of the rock above, forming "sinkholes", lake basins, and the like. The rates at which salt beds dissolve in a horizontal direction are estimated to range from a few millimeters to perhaps 10 cm (25 in) per year. Although the salt formations have been relatively stable for long periods of geologic time, fault zones through the beds are found. The age of the Permian salt deposits, for example, is over 200 million years.

Fig. B. This figure shows a typical sequence of sedimentary rocks and salt in a bedded salt formation. Some of the sedimentary beds, such as the dolomite and sandstone, could contain circulating groundwater. It is unlikely that the shale formation at depth would contain any significant quantities of moving water.

Fig. C. Bodies of salt are also formed in the shape of domes. Typically, the cross-section would look like a mushroom. The salt domes originate from thick beds of salt buried deep under layers of sedimentary rocks, at depths of 10 km (6-7 mi) or more. Because the salt is lighter in weight than the overlying sediments, a large amount of the salt shaped like a matchstick may slice its way upward through the sediments. This can be visualized as a long bubble of air rising upwards in a glass of water. When the salt reaches weaker sediments near the surface, it will spread outward and into the shape of a mushroom.

Salt domes in North America are located in the Gulf Coast area of the United States and along the eastern seaboard of Canada. The salt in the Gulf Coast domes originates from beds formed over 100 million years ago, probably in lagoons near an ocean. For this reason, the salt is quite pure and can be mined commercially. It is suggested that upward motion of the domes ceased about 30 million years ago. In general, the salt has not been actively dissolved by circulating groundwater in the surrounding sedimentary rock formations. The mushroom shape does provide traps for oil and natural gas.

Fig. D. Both salt domes and bedded salt formations occur in the Federal Republic of Germany. The salt domes are located in the northern part, near the sea coast. Some of these domes are really bedded salt formations which have been folded sharply upward by forces in the continental crust.

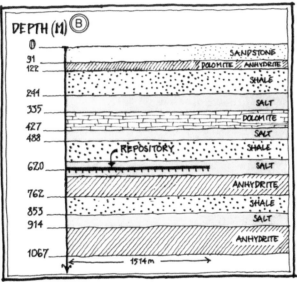

DEPTH (M)

0	SANDSTONE
91	DOLOMITE ANHYDRITE
122	SHALE
244	SALT
335	DOLOMITE
427	SALT
488	SHALE
	REPOSITORY
620	SALT
762	ANHYDRITE
853	SHALE
914	SALT
1067	ANHYDRITE

1514 m

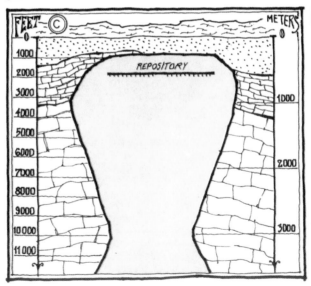

FEET — C — METERS

0	0
1000	REPOSITORY
2000	
3000	1000
4000	
5000	
6000	2000
7000	
8000	
9000	3000
10 000	
11 000	

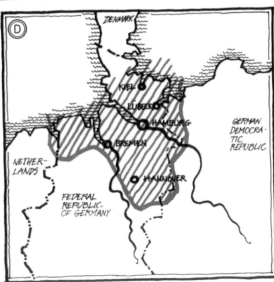

DENMARK

KIEL
LÜBECK
HAMBURG
BREMEN
NETHER-LANDS
HANNOVER

GERMAN DEMOCRA-TIC REPUBLIC

FEDERAL REPUBLIC OF GERMANY

The Formation of Groundwater

Water in nature is caught in a closed cycle of condensation and evaporation. Groundwater in the earth's crust represents the underground part of the cycle. It is formed directly from rainfall and melted snow, which flows down into the soil and rock, or by other surface water such as rivers, lakes, and oceans. This is called "infiltration". Water escapes to the atmosphere through vegetation and by evaporation of surface water.

The amount of water infiltration depends on the number of connected voids, cracks, and fractures in the surface soil and rock. Some rocks, such as granite, basalt, and tuff, may have an abundance of vertical joints and fractures. Large crushed zones in granitic rocks can also serve as excellent infiltration zones. Sometimes, however, these rocks may only have a relatively few cracks, or be located in mountainous areas. In these cases, the speed of the water runoff may not permit substantial infiltration. Many sandstones and often limestones have systems of well-connected voids or pores, as well as vertical cracks near the surface. This, of course, would allow water infiltration, even when the relief was irregular or steep. Shales may have some surface cracks and joints, but commonly few pores which are connected continuously. An abundance of clay minerals will inhibit water infiltration due to their swelling characteristic when wet.

The infiltrated water flows downward through the soil and rock to the groundwater table. In virgin rock, all connected joints, fractures, and pores are filled with water or fully "saturated". We know that the water pressure anywhere on the bottom of a lake is due to the weight of water above. It is exactly the same situation in the saturated rock below the groundwater table. If the ground surface were perfectly flat over an entire continent and the condensation-evaporation conditions were exactly the same everywhere, then the groundwater table would also be perfectly flat.

When the table is flat, the groundwater below it will not move through the pores, fractures, and joints in the rock. We know that this is not the case. Continents have mountains and plains, with different amounts of rainfall and vegetation. In wet and humid climates, the shape of the groundwater table will approximately match the general contour of the land surface. Because of these conditions over a large land region, the groundwater table will be inclined, or slightly tilted. Correspondingly, the water pressure in the rock at the same elevation will be different from one end to the other of the region. This pressure difference, known as the "regional groundwater pressure gradient", will cause the groundwater to flow through the rock toward the area of lower pressure. The gradient is commonly expressed in terms of meters of elevation difference per kilometer of horizontal distance in the table.

Because of hills and valleys distributed over a land region, the "local groundwater pressure gradient" from locality to locality will differ somewhat from the regional gradient. The regional pressure difference is really an average of all the local pressure differences. This is why some farms and towns may have more springs and better water wells than do their neighbors in other parts of the region.

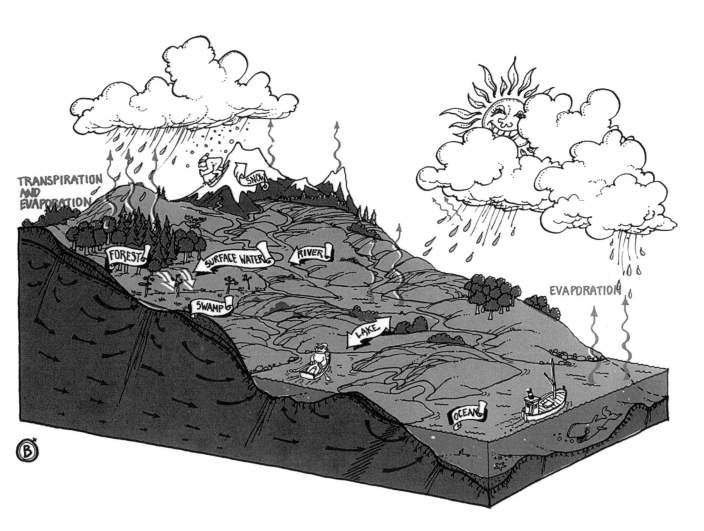

TRANSPIRATION AND EVAPORATION

SNOW

FOREST

SURFACE WATER

RIVER

SWAMP

LAKE

OCEAN

EVAPORATION

The Quantity and Velocity of Groundwater Flow

The quantity of groundwater flowing through a given cross-sectional area depends on the pressure difference and the resistance to flow. For example, the time necessary to fill a bucket with water from a garden hose depends on the pressure of the faucet and the length and diameter of the hose. The hose offers some resistance to the flow because the water drags on the inside wall of the hose. Similarly, the walls of rock fractures, pores, and the conduits between pores also exert a dragging action on the flowing groundwater.

A fundamental property of rock is its ability to transmit water. This property is known as the "hydraulic conductivity" or "flow conductivity", and it can be thought of as being a measure of the resistance to water flow in a rock mass. The flow velocity of water depends on the size of the cross-section available for letting a fixed quantity of water through. The smaller the area, the faster the water has to travel. In order to evaluate the safety of nuclear waste disposal in a particular rock mass, it is important to know the quantity, velocity, and chemical characteristics of the groundwater.

Fig. A. Let us assume that we place a cylinder of rock in a hypodermic syringe and the fit between the rock and glass wall is very tight. Now, imagine that water is poured into the space in the syringe between the rock and the plunger. When the plunger is pushed forward, the water will exert a pressure on the end of rock. The other end of the rock is open to the air. Thus, we have created a pressure difference or gradient between the two ends and water will flow through the rock and into the beaker. The quantity of water that will flow through the rock depends on three things: (1) the pressure gradient across the length of the rock cylinder; (2) the cross-sectional area of the rock cylinder; and (3) the flow conductivity of the rock.

Fig. B. We can imagine this experiment being performed on a much larger scale. The rock cylinder is now some tens of meters in diameter and length and resides deep in the earth below the groundwater table. The pressure difference between the two ends is now due to the regional pressure difference existing in the groundwater (as explained on page 18). The quantity of water flow through this very large rock cylinder depends exactly on the same three things cited above in the syringe experiment.

Fig. C. One important difference exists between the very small rock cylinder in the syringe and the very large rock cylinder in the earth. The small cylinder contains only connected pores. The large cylinder contains these pores and also fractures and joints. In hard rock, such as granite and basalt, the groundwater will flow almost entirely through the fractures and joints because the pores are few in number and poorly connected. In sedimentary rock, the water will flow principally through the connected pores as they are relatively more abundant and fractures and joints are less common. In nature, the flow conductivity generally decreases with depth. This is because the weight of the overburden rock tends to close the pores, fractures, and joints. Consequently, the quantity of groundwater flow will also decrease with depth. Finally, we mention that the flow direction at depth will be essentially horizontal, as the regional pressure difference is influenced less by the local pressure differences near the surface.

Fig. D. As mentioned previously, the groundwater flow velocity depends on the cross-sectional area available for it to flow through. In sedimentary rocks, the available area for water flow, or the porosity, is principally due to the volume of voids and pores, expressed as a percentage

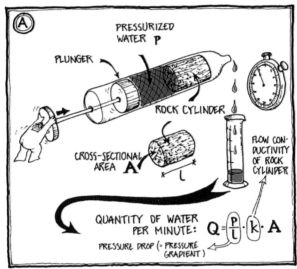

A

PRESSURIZED WATER **P**

PLUNGER

ROCK CYLINDER

CROSS-SECTIONAL AREA **A**

l

FLOW CONDUCTIVITY OF ROCK CYLINDER

QUANTITY OF WATER PER MINUTE: $Q = \dfrac{P}{l} \cdot k \cdot A$

PRESSURE DROP (= PRESSURE GRADIENT)

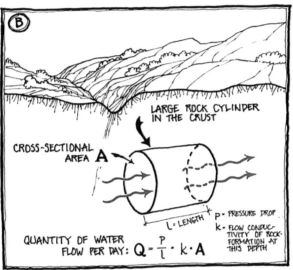

B

LARGE ROCK CYLINDER IN THE CRUST

CROSS-SECTIONAL AREA **A**

L = LENGTH

P = PRESSURE DROP

k = FLOW CONDUCTIVITY OF ROCK-FORMATION AT THIS DEPTH

QUANTITY OF WATER FLOW PER DAY: $Q = \dfrac{P}{l} \cdot k \cdot A$

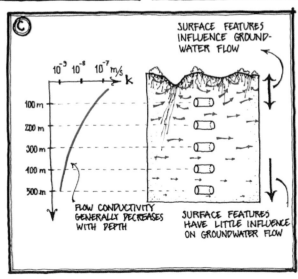

C

SURFACE FEATURES INFLUENCE GROUNDWATER FLOW

10^{-9} 10^{-8} 10^{-7} m/s   k

100 m
200 m
300 m
400 m
500 m

FLOW CONDUCTIVITY GENERALLY DECREASES WITH DEPTH

SURFACE FEATURES HAVE LITTLE INFLUENCE ON GROUNDWATER FLOW

of the total volume. In hard rocks, the area is essentially due to the fractures and joints, and is known as the "effective crack porosity". When the quantity of flowing water is constant, the flow velocity must increase as the effective crack porosity decreases and vice versa. Thus the flow velocity can be relatively fast at great depth even though there are few joints and fractures. How fast is "fast"? Perhaps 10 m per year (33 ft per year). Because the number of fractures and cracks varies considerably throughout a large rock mass, the local flow velocity will also vary. The regional flow velocity at any depth will be the average of all the local velocities. This average velocity will be small, maybe 2 or 3 m per year (5–10 ft per year). In any case, the amount of water moving through hard rock of 10 m by 10 m (33 ft by 33 ft) at a depth of 500 m (1600 ft), the quantity will be 1 liter (1 qt) per year, more or less.

As mentioned throughout this book, bodies of salt do not contain groundwater. What little water there may be, commonly much less than 1%, is contained as small individual droplets of brine within the salt crystals, or along the boundaries between crystals. Occasionally pockets of brine may be found in bedded salt. However, there are no pressure differences like those that exist in the groundwater in hard and sedimentary rocks. The brine droplets do not flow through the salt like groundwater. In fact, it is thought that they may remain fixed in place in their natural environment for perhaps hundreds of thousands of years.

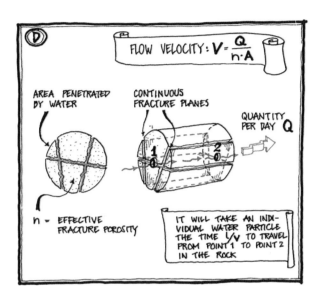

D

FLOW VELOCITY: $V = \dfrac{Q}{n \cdot A}$

AREA PENETRATED BY WATER

CONTINUOUS FRACTURE PLANES

QUANTITY PER DAY **Q**

n = EFFECTIVE FRACTURE POROSITY

IT WILL TAKE AN INDIVIDUAL WATER PARTICLE THE TIME L/V TO TRAVEL FROM POINT 1 TO POINT 2 IN THE ROCK

Groundwater Flow Near the Repository

In large bodies of sedimentary rock containing salt formations, the groundwater flows over, under, or around the salt, but never through it under natural circumstances. The flowing water in the sedimentary rocks may, of course, dissolve away the outside edges of the salt. This does occur in nature, but only very slowly. Groundwater could flow through a repository in salt if violent fracturing of the earth's crust took place at some future time in geologic history. This situation and its consequences will be discussed later in the book. For now, we shall discuss only paths for groundwater flows in hard rock masses containing joints and fractures.

The widths of fractures and joint openings vary from locality to locality. They generally decrease with depth in the earth's crust. This is due to the weight of the overburden rock. These widths are commonly small, perhaps less than 0.5 mm (0.02 in). The quantity of flowing water decreases significantly with decreasing width. If the fracture width decreases by 50%, the quantity can be reduced by more than 30%. A 90% decrease in width reduces the flow more than 99%.

Many hard rock masses exhibit sizable zones of fractures in which the major amount of groundwater flow is located. This has been verified by observations in many deep mines and power tunnels.

Fig. A. Let us assume that a repository site is located in an area surrounded by valleys. These valleys represent zones of weakness in the subsurface rock mass. These zones are considered "weak" because they contain an abundance of fractures. Erosion of the surface rock by glaciation and water runoff occurs more rapidly over geologic time, and valleys are formed.

Fig. B. The repository is located in a block of "solid" rock. That is, there are fewer fractures and joints, and more widely scattered, than in the zones of weakness which surround the block. Most of the groundwater flows through the zones of weakness because they are paths of least resistance. Some water does flow through the block, but only very little by comparison.

Fig. C. Because of the hills and valleys and the average slope of the ground surface, the paths of groundwater flow may be quite complicated in the deep fracture zones. Closer to the ground surface, the shape of the landscape has a dominating influence on the pattern of flow paths.

Fig. D. The groundwater movement in the block containing the repository depends on the water pressure and the amount of water in the surrounding zones of weakness as well as on the water infiltrating downward from the surface. Below a depth of some 500 m, water flow from these zones into the joints and fractures in the block will be more significant than water infiltration from the surface.

In searching for a repository site, it is important to avoid rock masses with many zones of weakness containing relatively large amounts of water. Substantial amounts of groundwater flow could accelerate the corrosion of the metal canisters and leaching of the wastes.

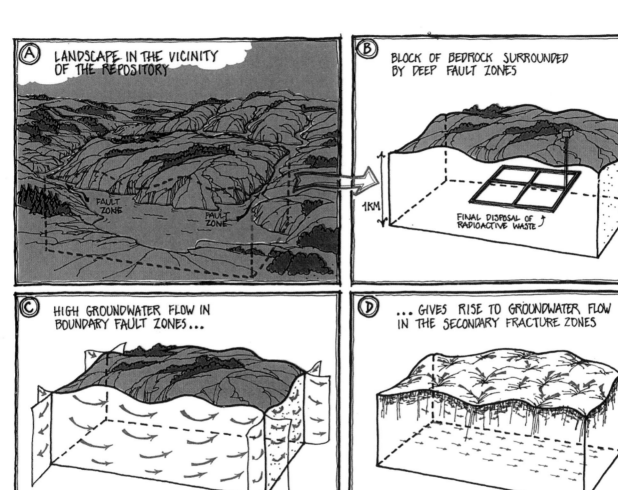

Groundwater Flow Through the Disposal Rooms and to the Surface

As mentioned on the preceding pages, we shall limit our comments to hard rock masses containing joints and fractures. It is quite likely that joint and fracture planes will intersect the drillholes containing waste canisters in a repository. Although the number and widths of the joints and fractures may be relatively small as compared to a zone of weakness, there will be groundwater flow. The quantity of flowing water in the vicinity of the drillholes will also be small, perhaps only about a liter (quart) per year. At this rate it would require approximately 150 years to collect enough water for a bath in the average size tub. One million years of water collection would be required to satisfy the needs of about five family households for only one year.

Although the quantities of water flow each year will be small, it must be recognized that water causes corrosion of metal. This means that eventually the wall of the metal canister will be corroded away and the groundwater will come into contact with the waste. When this happens, leaching of radionuclides from the waste will begin. How fast will the metal corrode? How long will it take the groundwater to leach the wastes, and in what quantities? The answers to these questions depend on many things. These include the canister metal, the waste form, the chemical nature of the groundwater, the amount and velocity of water flow around the canister, and the temperature.

The chemical make-up of the water will be representative of the minerals in the rock. This is why it has been proposed in Sweden to bury the spent fuel rods in copper-walled canisters in granite. The copper will be extremely resistant to corrosion by the chemicals in the Swedish groundwater, and should protect the spent fuel from the groundwater for thousands of years.

In each country, efforts are being made to develop and test backfill and canister materials which will be highly resistant to chemical corrosion by the groundwater in basalt, granite, and tuff. This is also the case for the brine which may collect around the waste canisters in salt. It is estimated from laboratory experiments that the glass form of the reprocessing wastes can be leached by groundwater at a rate of about 1 mm (0.04 in) every 2000 years. However, this rate varies with the chemical composition of the water. For certain types of water, the glass can be many times more leach-resistant than spent fuel.

In spite of all these precautions and good intentions, we must assume that the waste will be exposed to the groundwater. How could this happen, and what would be the consequences? We can speculate that the backfill material around the canister will be unable to provide the desired sealing effects for some unknown reason. A canister may be unknowingly damaged during fabrication, or handling and emplacement, or contain undetected flaws in the metal. Such things could create "zones of weakness" in the metal, which would accelerate the corrosion and expose the waste much sooner than expected. Finally, the high temperatures in the rock could promote chemical reactions in the water which would dissolve the wastes more quickly than originally thought. It is extremely unlikely that all canisters would suffer all these things simultaneously, but some could.

This, of course, will undoubtedly happen at some time in the future, regardless of the quality of the canister and backfill material. But now we are assuming that these events take place much sooner than thought possible. The radiation danger from the waste particles is still great because the time for decay of the radioactivity has been relatively short. What will happen?

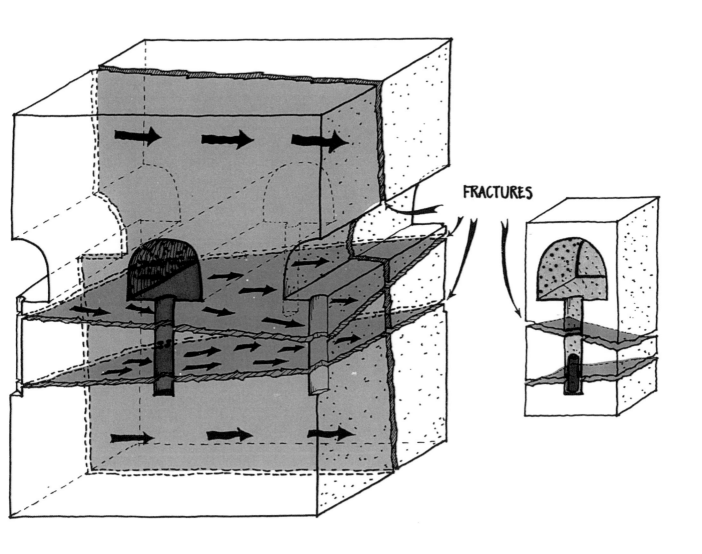

FRACTURES

The rock is the last barrier. Clearly, the groundwater will transport the radionuclides into the fractures and joints of the rock. It would be unreasonable to think that the water will suddenly rise through the rock to the ground surface at race-car speeds. For something like that to happen it would require a natural catastrophe of unbelievable proportions. In a later chapter, however, we do discuss such possibilities and their consequences.

For now, let us concentrate on the consequences of what we have suggested could happen. The radionuclides will be transported downstream from the repository and finally into the water circulating in the large zones of weakness in the rock mass. Because of regional pressure differences in the water, the radionuclides will be transported from one weakness zone to the next. Eventually, they will reach the groundwater near the surface and enter the water that may be used by living organisms.

What safeguards will the rock offer during this transport process? There are at least three: (1) the length of the *path* that a radionuclide must follow to the ground surface; (2) the dilution of the radionuclides by fresh water during the transportation; and (3) the chemical *retardation* of radionuclides by natural minerals in the rock. The path to the surface will be long and complicated by the intersecting fractures and joints. The distances will be relatively great, from a few to possibly hundreds of kilometers. For an average groundwater velocity of even 2 or 3 m (6–10 ft) per year, it will require at least a thousand years, and perhaps tens of thousands of years, for a radioactive particle to reach the surface. This time is sufficient for the radioactivities of some waste particles to decay to below harmful levels.

For other particles it is not enough time. During transport, radionuclides will be diluted by fresh waters from the surrounding rocks and from infiltration from surface waters. Local changes in the flow velocity due to more and then less fractures in the rock will improve the mixing. Although some radionuclides will still be dangerous by themselves, the levels of concentration can be decreased by dilution to less than those existing in nature.

Finally, there is the natural ability of minerals in rocks to attract radionuclide particles in such a way that they become attached to each other. This process is known as "sorbtion", and it retards the movement of the particles through the rock. The sorbtion abilities of rocks vary from rock type to rock type. Some are good, particularly when clay minerals coat the fracture walls as often happens in nature. Some are poor, such as relatively pure salt unless it contains thin layers of clay and shale.

What can we conclude from all of this? First, it is likely that sooner or later the metal and backfill barriers around the buried waste will fail and groundwater will leach the waste. Secondly, the waste form itself is a barrier because the leaching process is naturally slow and the available quantities of water for leaching are small.

Finally, the rock serves as the last barrier by offering long migration paths, dilution with fresh waters, and retardation of radionuclides by sorbtion from the natural minerals. This is *conceivable* why wastes from the natural fission reactors in the uranium deposits at Oklo appear to have remained localized in the nearby rocks for some 2 billion years as was discussed on page 6.

The Disturbed Rock and the Groundwater

Factors that Influence Groundwater Flow

Except for some future and unpredictable action by mankind, the only way in which the waste could become harmful to living organisms is by transport of the radionuclides to the earth's surface by circulating groundwaters. This, of course, requires that the metal *canisters* must be first damaged by some action of nature, such as faulting of the rock during an earthquake, or by corrosion from chemical reactions with the circulating groundwater in hard rock, or with brine in salt. The corrosion of the metal canisters will most certainly occur, but may require hundreds of years if chemically resistant metals, or buffer materials around the canisters, are used. Once the waste is exposed to the circulating groundwater, or to the brine, it must be dissolved, or chemically leached, into solution with the water. This leaching process is quite time consuming. This will be discussed in a later chapter of the book. The natural ability of the rock to absorb radionuclide particles as they migrate will also be explained. Now, however, we shall concentrate on describing the factors that can disturb the natural pattern of the groundwater circulation in the rock.

Previously (page 18) we have explained the circulation of the groundwater in hard rock containing joints and fractures and in sedimentary rock containing connected pores. The pressure differences in the groundwater, and the flow conductivity and porous nature of the rock, are important factors for evaluating the quantity and volume of water flow. The spacing, orientation, interconnection, and width of the joints and fractures are of special interest in hard rock. The diameter, length, and orientation of the tubes or "conduits", which connect pores in sedimentary rock, as well as the size of the pores themselves, are important. When the rock is fully saturated, the volume of water in a given mass of rock must equal the volume of the void spaces.

The widths of the joints and the diameters of the conduits and pores depend on the forces within the rock mass. These forces are due to the pressure of the water, the weight of the overburden rock, and any loadings because of nearby mountain ranges or movements of the "plates" in the earth's crust. When the temperature in the rock begins to rise due to the heat generated by the radioactive waste in the canisters, the rock will try to expand. However, since the warm rock is restricted from expanding by adjacent cooler rock, a uniform force is developed within the rock, and the fracture and pore openings located some distance from the disposal rooms will tend to close. This effect will make it more difficult for the water to flow through the rock. As the water in the rock is heated it flows easier (just as oil for an automobile engine flows easier as the temperature increases). This effect allows the water to flow through the rock with less resistance.

The heating of the water in the rock mass does directly influence the direction of movement of the groundwater. As water is heated, it becomes lighter and will move upward through the joints and pores. This is known as the "buoyancy effect" (just as warm air in a heated room collects near the ceiling and cold air collects near the floor). To the naked eye from a distance, the upward movement of the warm water and the simultaneous downward movement of the cold water would appear as circular motion of the water in the rock mass.

In hard rock, the disposal rooms and tunnels in a repository can act as a system of drainage pipes. Backfilling of the rooms and tunnels with a mixture of clay and crushed rock can reduce this water flow considerably, perhaps to the same degree as flow in the originally undisturbed rock. Excavation by blasting, even with careful control, will cause some fracturing of the rock in the roofs, floors, and walls of the rooms and tunnels. This fracturing will increase the hydraulic conductivity of the rock and provide potential paths along which the groundwater can move. In salt, which contains virtually no water as compared to even hard rock, fracturing during excavation can be controlled exceptionally well by the use of continuous mining machines. In the near future, such machines may be practical to use even in hard rocks.

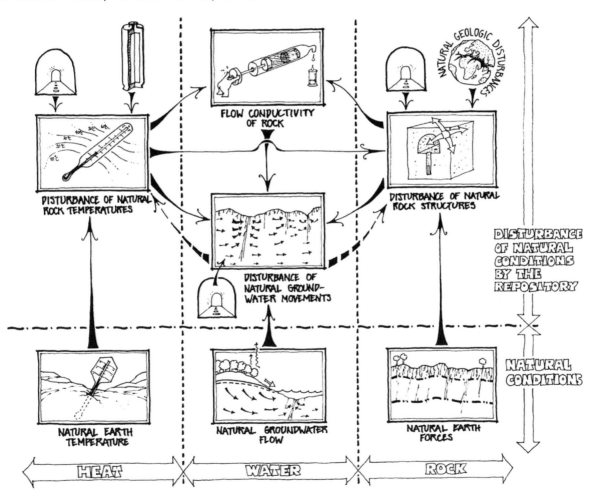

FLOW CONDUCTIVITY OF ROCK

NATURAL GEOLOGIC DISTURBANCES

DISTURBANCE OF NATURAL ROCK TEMPERATURES

DISTURBANCE OF NATURAL GROUND-WATER MOVEMENTS

DISTURBANCE OF NATURAL ROCK STRUCTURES

DISTURBANCE OF NATURAL CONDITIONS BY THE REPOSITORY

NATURAL EARTH TEMPERATURE

NATURAL GROUNDWATER FLOW

NATURAL EARTH FORCES

NATURAL CONDITIONS

HEAT   WATER   ROCK

Influence of Repository Construction on Groundwater Flow

The construction of the repository involves excavation of the shafts, tunnels, and rooms, drilling of boreholes for placement of the waste canisters, and backfilling and sealing of all mined openings. These activities may cause considerable disturbance of the natural pattern of groundwater circulation in hard rock mass, but little if any disturbance in sedimentary rock formations around a large body of salt. The following discussion applies only to repositories in bodies of hard rock, and does not consider the influence of the heat generated by the radioactive waste.

Fig. A. Before the repository is constructed, a balance exists between the water infiltration at the ground surface and the water circulation in the rock mass.

Fig. B. During construction of the repository, water flows from the rock mass into the tunnels and rooms, and must be pumped to the surface. More than likely, the water infiltration at the ground surface, and the natural water movement in the rock mass toward the repository, will not be sufficient to replace the water loss to the tunnels and rooms. Thus, the groundwater table above the repository moves downward. If the rock mass has relatively few joints and fractures, the volume of water in the rock is small and the groundwater level may sink rapidly.

Fig. C. When the construction of the repository is finished, say in perhaps 10 years, the overlying rock will probably be drained free of water. We would certainly expect this complete drainage to occur if the rooms and tunnels are not backfilled for some 25 years after emplacement of the waste canisters. Thus, it is highly probable that the groundwater table will move from close to the earth's surface to the immediate vicinity of the repository. This region of water drainage in the rock mass is known as the "drawdown zone".

Fig. D. When pumping water to the surface is stopped and the rooms, tunnels, and shafts are filled and sealed, the drawdown zone in the rock above the repository will slowly become saturated again with water. This process, known as "recharging" of the drawdown zone, must take place over a time period of perhaps 200 years in order for the groundwater to reach its original, pre-repository level. Because of air trapped in the backfilling material in the tunnels and rooms, the joints and fractures in the immediate vicinity of the repository may become only partially saturated.

During the recharging of the drawdown zone, the direction of the water flow is principally towards the repository. Of course, as the groundwater level rises toward the earth's surface, there will be some groundwater circulation through the rock mass which contains the repository. Consequently, for some period of time (perhaps several or more decades or even a century) groundwater transport of any substantial amount of radionuclides from a damaged waste canister into the rock mass would be quite unlikely.

Some hard rock masses, such as basalt and tuff, are formed as relatively horizontal layers which may exhibit differing degrees and amounts of jointing and fracturing, as well as differing values of flow conductivity. Some layers may be very "tight" with few joints and fractures. As a consequence, a limited drawdown zone may develop immediately above the repository. Near the earth's surface, the groundwater table may drop only slightly, if at all. In other words, there could exist layers of rock between the earth's surface and the repository in which the groundwater flows are not significantly disturbed.

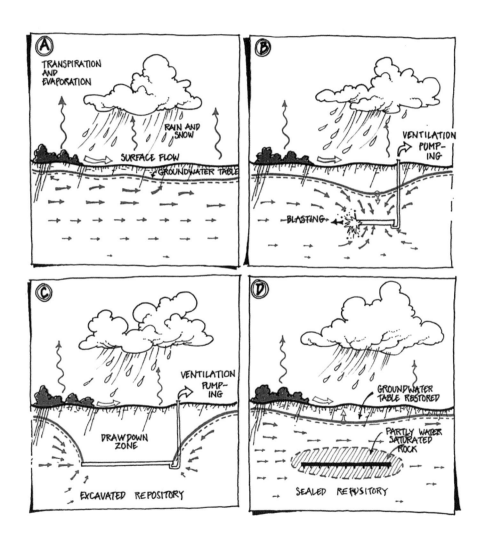

33

Disturbance of the Natural Temperatures in the Rock

The temperatures on the earth's surface at a depth of only a few feet is approximately equal to the average annual temperature for the regional climate. The temperature in the earth's crust increases naturally with increasing depth below the surface. This increase, known as the "geothermal gradient", varies from locality to locality throughout the world, but averages about 30°C per km (26°F per 1000 ft). In Sweden, for example, the temperature at a depth of 500 m (1600 ft) in the granite is about 15°C (60°F). This compares with a temperature of perhaps 30°C (85°F) at the same depth in salt formations in the United States.

The heat from the radioactive waste will cause an increase in the temperature of the rock in the repository. This increase can be controlled by changing the spacing between emplaced waste canisters or by ventilation of the disposal rooms for some years after emplacement. The thermal power, or heat generation rate, of the waste decreases with time. Thus, the waste canisters can be cooled in water pools on the surface for some years prior to disposal. In Sweden, the plan is to cool the canisters of reprocessing wastes for 40 years prior to disposal in the repository. The United States concept for spent fuel disposal requires that the fuel elements be cooled for at least 10 years after removal from a reactor. The emplacement of the waste canisters in a system of disposal rooms subjects the rock mass to an average heat load.

Fig. A. In the Swedish disposal concept for granite, the reprocessing waste canisters would be placed in drillholes spaced 4 m (13 ft) apart along the length of a room. On the other hand, the spent-fuel canisters would be spaced 6 m (20 ft). Since the thermal power of each waste form is different at the time of emplacement, the spacing must be different in order to obtain a common heat loading of 5.25 W/m² (21 kW/acre). This loading is approximately equivalent to the heat generated by seven 100 W light bulbs in a 130 m² (1500 ft²) house. About 10 years after emplacement, a maximum temperature increase of about 40°C (104°F) will occur in the granite immediately next to the canister. Thereafter the temperature in the rock will decrease. It will take approximately 10,000 years for the rock temperature to return to the original 15°C for the reprocessing waste, and perhaps as long as 100,000 years for the spent fuel.

Fig. B. Approximately 50 years are required for the heated zone to extend into the granite some 100 m above and below the disposals rooms, and 600 years to extend about 400 m. After 600 years, the temperature in the rock around the waste canisters is about 20°C greater than the original temperature.

Fig. C. The reference disposal concept for salt in the United States considers a heat load of 25 W/m² (100 kW/acre). This heat load is equivalent to about thirty-four 100 W light bulbs in a 130 m² (1500 ft) house. The reprocessing waste canisters would have a thermal power of 2160 W each, and would be placed in a single row of drillholes spaced 3.66 m (12 ft) apart.

The spent-fuel canisters, with a thermal power of 550 W each, would be placed in two rows of drillholes in a disposal room, with 1.67 m (5ft) spacing between rows and drillholes. These configurations would cause a maximum temperature increase of about 125°C in the salt for reprocessing waste, and 105°C for spent fuel.

Fig. D. An earlier concept considered the use of a salt dome for a reprocessing waste repository, with a disposal room depth of 610 m (2000 ft) and heat load of 37 W/m²

(150 kW/acre). After about 500 years, the heated zone will penetrate into the sedimentary rock formations above and near the top of the dome.

Thermal conductivity, a fundamental property of all materials, represents a resistance by the material to the flow of heat through it. Insulation is used in the construction of a house because its low thermal conductivity, or high resistance to heat flow, reduces the heat loss through the walls during the winter. Because different rock types have different thermal conductivities, the maximum temperature rise will be different for the same heat load in salt, granite, basalt, tuff, and shale.

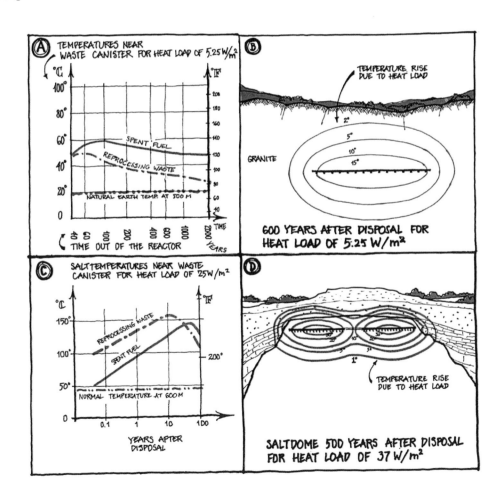

(A) TEMPERATURES NEAR WASTE CANISTER FOR HEAT LOAD OF 5.25 W/m²

SPENT FUEL
REPROCESSING WASTE
NATURAL EARTH TEMP. AT 500 M

TIME OUT OF THE REACTOR

(B) GRANITE

TEMPERATURE RISE DUE TO HEAT LOAD

600 YEARS AFTER DISPOSAL FOR HEAT LOAD OF 5.25 W/m²

(C) SALT TEMPERATURES NEAR WASTE CANISTER FOR HEAT LOAD OF 25 W/m²

REPROCESSING WASTE
SPENT FUEL
NORMAL TEMPERATURE AT 600 M

YEARS AFTER DISPOSAL

(D) TEMPERATURE RISE DUE TO HEAT LOAD

SALTDOME 500 YEARS AFTER DISPOSAL FOR HEAT LOAD OF 37 W/m²

35

Disturbance of the Structure of the Rock

Thermal expansion, a basic property of all materials, represents the ability of a material to expand its volume when heated and to contract when cooled. This characteristic is the reason for placing expansion joints in bridge decks. Without such joints, the tensile force created by contraction of the steel and concrete during cold weather would cause the fastener pins and rivets to break. During hot weather, the compressive force created by the expansion would cause the bridge deck and structural members to buckle or shear off. Such may also be the case in the repository rock mass if the heat load from the emplaced waste is too great. At the least, the heat will cause some of the fractures and voids in the rock to close.

Fig. A. When the rock is heated, its natural reaction is to try to expand. When compressive forces are applied to all sides of a cube of rock, it is possible to prevent the volume expansion. For such a situation, each and every element of rock inside the cube experiences forces equal to those applied on the outside faces.

Fig. B. The rock tries to expand immediately when the heat from the emplaced waste canisters flows into it. However, this expansion is restricted by the neighboring rock around the borehole, which is also trying to expand, and by the cooler rock some distance away. Since the expansion is restricted, compressive forces are developed within the rock. As the heat flows further into the rock surrounding the entire disposal room, the compressive forces develop simultaneously.

Fig. C. Before the disposal rooms and boreholes for the waste canisters are excavated, each element of rock is subjected to a natural state of compression. The forces are due to the weight of the overburden rock and to loadings from past geologic history. After excavation, these forces are redistributed in the rock mass around the rooms and boreholes. After emplacement of the waste canisters, the forces developed in the rock by heating are added to the forces previously existing in the rock. If the resultant forces become large enough, the hard rock may develop new fractures, or blocks or rocks on either sides of joints and fractures may move by different amounts. On the other hand, the salt will flow like a plastic substance. If the movements due to flow are quite large, the salt may rupture and develop fracture.

Fig. D. If the disposal rooms are backfilled with crushed rock and clay soon after the waste canisters are emplaced, then this material will provide support to the rock as it tries to expand during heating. If this restraint is not provided, blocks of rocks may break loose from the hard rock mass and fall into the rooms. In salt, the rooms would begin to close by plastic flow, with slabs breaking loose from the roof and walls if the movements are quite large. This situation is known as "room instability". Instability can be minimized or eliminated by installing steel bolts in drillholes in the rock around the openings, and by backfilling soon after emplacement of the waste canisters.

The above discussions have concentrated on the effects of heating in the rock mass around the disposal rooms. Far above and below the rooms, the heating also generates additional forces within the rock mass. If the heat load from the emplaced waste is too great, the forces may create additional fractures in the rock formations. This could permit a greater communication of groundwater in the vertical direction. Since the rock is unrestrained at the earth's surface, the ground will slowly rise, perhaps a meter or so over a period of several thousand years. As the heat from the waste is dissipated from the rock into the atmosphere, the ground surface will slowly fall to approximately its original elevation. The temperature increase at the earth's surface will be perhaps 1°C (approximately 2°F).

It is possible to predict the approximate limits of these effects for a given rock mass and waste form. They can be minimized by reducing the initial heat load in the repository.

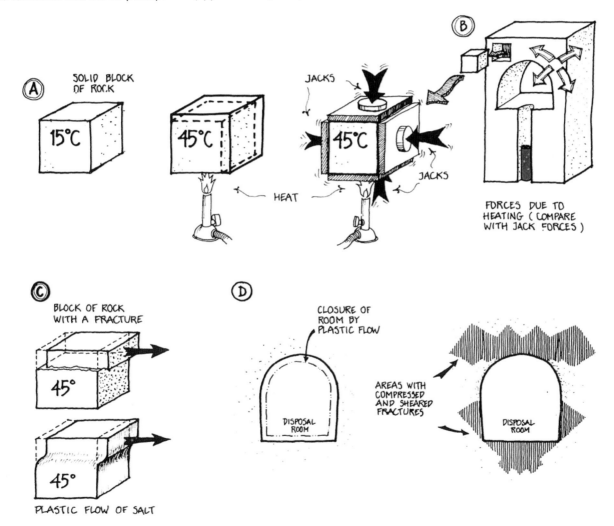

(A) SOLID BLOCK OF ROCK
15°C
45°C
45°C JACKS
HEAT
JACKS

(B) FORCES DUE TO HEATING (COMPARE WITH JACK FORCES)

(C) BLOCK OF ROCK WITH A FRACTURE
45°
45°
PLASTIC FLOW OF SALT

(D) CLOSURE OF ROOM BY PLASTIC FLOW
DISPOSAL ROOM
AREAS WITH COMPRESSED AND SHEARED FRACTURES
DISPOSAL ROOM

NWD - C

Disturbance of Groundwater Flow in the Rock

When water is heated in a kettle on the kitchen stove, the warmer water at the bottom will continuously move upward and be replaced by cooler water moving downward from the top. This is because water becomes lighter when it is heated. This buoyancy effect will also occur in the groundwater around a repository. The heated water will have a tendency to move upward through joints and connected pores in the rock mass, and be replaced by cooler water from above and from the sides. This circular movement of water is known as a "convection cell", so-called "regional gradients".

Since the earth's surface is not perfectly level, there will always be differences in the groundwater pressure. This is why water flows in a river from the mountains to the plains. Such is also the case in hard rock and sedimentary rock formations when they contain water-saturated joints, fractures, and connected pores. Even if the ground surface is quite level, say only a few meters of elevation change per kilometer, the regional pressure differences will cause the groundwater to move faster in the horizontal direction as compared to the vertical flow induced by heat from the waste.

Fig. A. Let us assume that the ground surface above a repository is perfectly level for thousands of kilometers in all directions, and remains level for 1000 years. This means that the regional pressure differences in the hard rock mass would be practically nonexistent, and the groundwater would remain stationary in the undisturbed rock away from the repository. The heat from the buried waste for a heat load of 5.25 W/m² (21 kW/acre) would create a large convection cell through each half of the repository, and heated water would move upwards to the earth's surface. The cell could conceivably extend a kilometer below and to each side of the repository.

Fig. B. For the same situation as discussed in Fig. A, let us now consider the more natural situation in which there is a regional pressure difference in the rock mass. This gradient is taken as 0.2%, corresponding to an average decrease in groundwater table elevation of 2 m for every 1 km of horizontal distance (approximately 10-11 ft for every mile). Since the water velocity in the convection cell is much less than that due to the regional pressure difference, the convective cells are "swept away" by the horizontal groundwater flow. All that remains is a small "ripple" or wave in the flow as it passes through the rock mass which contains the buried waste.

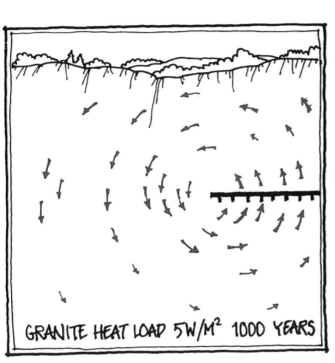

GRANITE HEAT LOAD 5W/M² 1000 YEARS

GRANITE HEAT LOAD 5W/M² 1000 YEARS

1KM

A

B

Disturbance of Groundwater Flow in the Rock Around a Salt Formation

Fig. A. For comparative purposes we now consider the disturbance of the groundwater flow in the sedimentary rock formations surrounding a salt dome. As before, it is assumed that the ground surface is perfectly level and the regional pressure difference is nonexistent. The heat from the buried reprocessing waste for a heat load of 37 W/m² (150 kW/acre) will cause convection cells to develop in the sedimentary rock above and on the upper flanks of the dome after 500 years. There is no groundwater in the salt, and consequently no disturbance by the heating.

Fig. B. For the salt dome discussed in Fig. A, a more natural situation would be one in which the regional pressure difference in the sedimentary rocks was 0.06% (60 cm elevation change every 1 km, or 3 ft for every mile). The convection cells on the upstream flank of the dome and on the top are swept away by the regional flow and replaced by a rippling or wavy motion in the flow. The convection cell on the downstream flank of the dome is reduced in size, but nevertheless remains. These disturbances in the groundwater flow will diminish and nearly vanish after 1000 years, as the heat produced by the buried waste becomes very small.

If convection cells develop and persist in the groundwater system around a repository in hard rock, the radionuclides may be leached from damaged waste canisters and transported to the ground surface. The velocity of the groundwater moving upward in the cell will be small, perhaps 1 m per year (3 ft per year). Thus for a repository depth of 500 m (1600 ft) it would take some 500 years for any radionuclides to escape to the surface. For a repository in salt, the circular motion of the convection cells would tend to dissolve the salt along the top and around the flanks of the dome. This process could reduce the thickness of the salt barrier between the sedimentary rock and the buried waste. It is quite unlikely that the regional pressure gradient would disappear in an area in which it has been rather firmly established by nature over the past thousands and tens of thousands of years. Thus, the likelihood of large convection cells being developed is extremely small. To further minimize the chance for development of convection cells, the heat load in the repository can be reduced by increasing the spacing between buried canisters of waste. In the case of the salt dome repository discussed in Fig. D, the convection cell on the downstream flank of the dome will essentially disappear if the heat load is reduced by 30% or 40%.

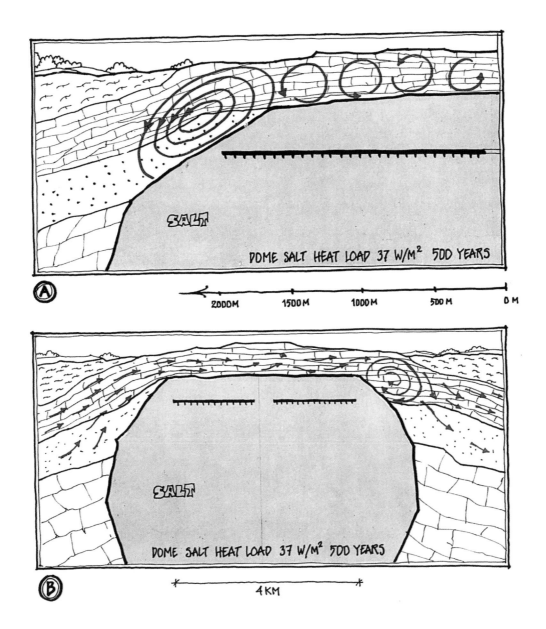

A DOME SALT HEAT LOAD 37 W/M² 500 YEARS

2000M   1500M   1000M   500M   0 M

B DOME SALT HEAT LOAD 37 W/M² 500 YEARS

4 KM

41

Long-term Behavior of the Rock and the Groundwater

The Long-term Stability of the Rock Structure

Movements of the continents, future ice ages, and erosion of the surface rock influence the natural forces that exist in the rock. Changes in these forces, even over long time periods, may cause additional fracturing in the rock masses. This future disturbance of the natural structure of the rock is important if it should occur in regions where nuclear waste repositories were located. We would not expect any severe disturbances to occur in repository areas because these rocks are selected on the basis of their histories of relative peace and quiet over the past millions of years. As an example, let us consider the past geologic history of the granitic rock in Sweden, and speculate on its future history over the next half a million years or so.

Fig. A. The part of the earth's crust represented by Sweden dates back from the most part to the Precambrian time period. This period of geologic history ended more than 900 million years ago. The oldest rock, approximately 2 billion years, occurs in the southwest part of the country, as indicated by the circled (1) in the figure. Between the rocks of different ages, e.g. between (1) and (2), deep penetrating seams are found. The Precambrian mountain ranges were totally eroded away about 600 million years ago. At that time, the land was part of the ocean floor. Layers of new sedimentary rocks were formed on an almost flat surface. The sedimentary rocks in, for example, southern Sweden and on Gotland, were formed this way.

The layering in these rocks has remained horizontal since its formation. This would indicate that the underlying shield has remained unchanged, or motionless, in these locations over the past 600 million years.

Time periods of less than a million years are required for the radiation in nuclear waste to decay to below the natural radiation levels that currently exist. On the basis of past geologic history over 600 million years, it would not seem reasonable to forecast major movements, erosion, or fracturing in the shield.

Fig. B. However, movements and displacements have occurred in the largest fracture and joint zones of the shield. The forces that exist between the different rock formations of great size in Sweden probably cause these movements.

The most well known of these movements has taken place along the Svedala fault in Skåne, approximately 2 km (3 mi) in 600 million years. Another fault zone in Skåne is the Vällinge fault, which has experienced only a tenth of the displacement that has occurred along the Svedala fault. Measurements along other faults in the Precambrian shield have indicated substantially smaller displacements. For two faults in Uppland and Småland, displacements of only 15 and 30 cm (6 and 12 in), respectively, in 600 million years were measured.

Fig. C. Since the last Ice Age ended some 10,000 years ago, the ground surface has risen several hundred meters (approximately 1000 ft). The greatest uplift has taken place in northern Sweden. Here, the rate of upward movement is about 1 m (3 ft) every century. On the other hand, the ground surface is moving downward in southern Sweden. (The numbers on the figure indicate rate of verical movement in millimeters per year, with + upward and - downward). The uplift occurs in a somewhat irregular fashion, and cause movements in the deep fault zones in the shield.

So, what does this all mean to the safety of nuclear waste disposal in rock? Essentially, the best forecast of future geologic events in a region must be based on the observable events during the past. It is highly probable that a large rock mass will remain geologically stable over the next hundreds of thousands of years if it has been stable for the last millions of years. The efforts for locating possible sites for repositories are concentrating on finding such rock masses.

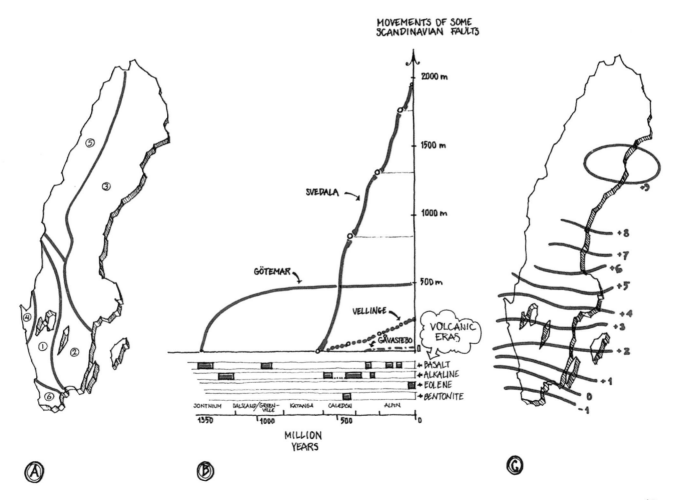

The Long-term Behavior of the Groundwater Flow

We must be able to forecast the long-term behavior of the groundwater circulation in rock masses containing repositories. This is certainly as important as being able to forecast the long-term stability of the rock structure. Violent faulting or fracturing of the rock mass by forces in the earth's crust may damage a repository in the long-term future. However, it will be the groundwater that will transport the radionuclides to the ground surface. The climate will determine how much water is available for infiltration into the rock, and influence the level of the groundwater table.

Fig. A. In humid climates the large infiltration of precipitated water will bring the groundwater table close to the surface. A landscape with rolling hills will cause relatively strong movements of the groundwater in the heavily fractured and jointed rock near the surface. At greater depths, where the rock is tighter with fewer fractures and joints, it is the average slope of the groundwater table over a large distance that causes the circulation and flow of the water. The irregular shape of the table near the surface has little if any effect on the flow at greater depths. The flow velocity of great depth is much less than in the rocks near the surface.

Fossils of living organisms from past geologic times can be studied to determine the variations in the climatic conditions. In Northern Europe and America, for example, the fossils tell us that all types of climates have existed. These include both dry desert-like and hot humid climates, and ice ages with glaciers several kilometers thick. Climate changes like these will probably occur during the time period required for isolation of nuclear wastes in a repository.

Fig. B. In a dry, desert-like climate, the groundwater table will move downward, and the landscape will have little influence on the groundwater flow in the rocks near the surface.

Fig. C. In a very humid, tropical climate, water will accumulate in ponds and lakes, and perhaps even cause the oceans to rise. This condition will cause the groundwater table to flatten or become more horizontal. There will be less water movement in the rock because the regional pressure differences will be smaller.

Fig. D. During an ice age, the groundwater in the rocks near the ground surface will be frozen and motionless. In the deeper rock, the groundwater will flow slower than before or after the ice age.

On the basis of the above discussions, it would seem that climatic changes from a humid climate will probably not significantly increase the groundwater flow. In fact, periods of tropical climates and glaciation could reduce the velocity of the groundwater circulation through the repository. Disturbance of the rock structure by changes of the forces in the earth's crust would appear to have more influence on the groundwater circulation than climatic changes on the surface.

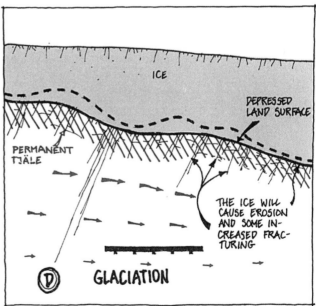

47

Nuclear Waste Leakage into the Groundwater

Movement of Radionuclides

On several previous occasions in this book we have discussed the movement of radioactive particles with the groundwater as it moves through the rock. Radionuclide migration is the central issue in the nuclear waste disposal. This phenomenon is now discussed in more detail.

The so-called "waste package" is composed of the waste form, the metal canister, and a clay or clay crushed rock mixture which fills the space between the canister and the rock wall of the drillhole.

Soon after the waste canisters are emplaced, the groundwater will start to penetrate into the backfill material. After all of the disposal rooms, tunnels, and shafts to the surface have been back-filled and sealed, recharging of the drawdown zone above the repository will begin in earnest.

Although the backfill material surrounding the waste canister will restrict the flow of groundwater, the outer wall of the canister eventually will become saturated. As soon as the water makes contact with the canister, the metal will begin to corrode. Depending upon the amount of water flow, its chemical make-up, and the temperature, the corrosion will eventually eat a path through the metal and come into contact with the waste. The waste will begin to dissolve, however, quite slowly. It has been estimated from laboratory tests that only about one millimeter will be leached from reprocessing waste glass every 2000 years. Since the clay mixture has a very low flow conductivity, it will be difficult for the radionuclides to flow away from the canister. In addition, some of the radionuclides particles will attach themselves to the clay particles by the process of "sorbtion".

Some radioactive particles will be transported through the backfill material to the rock. The groundwater will carry the radionuclides into fractures and joints in the rock around the drillhole. The minerals naturally contained as filling materials within the fractures and joints will sorb some of the radionuclides as they move with the groundwater. Thus, when a water particle and a radionuclide particle begin their travels at the edge of the drillhole, the water particle will reach the surface of the earth faster than the radionuclide particle. Depending upon the lengths of the flow paths to the surface, the radionuclide particle could arrive some tens and perhaps hundreds of years after the arrival of the water particle.

The concentrations of radionuclides along a path to the ground surface will be continually diluted by fresh waters moving into the area from the sides and above the path. Provided certain chemical conditions exist, the radionuclides could be deposited in the fractures and joints during groundwater flow.

Even in the worst situation, involving an early exposure of the waste form to the circulating groundwater, it appears highly unlikely that any radionuclides could migrate from the repository to the ground surface in less than a few thousands of years. It is much more likely that the travel times will be of the order of tens of thousands of years due to the combination of retardation of radioactive particles and the extremely long paths through the fractures and joints.

Even if the radionuclides reach the surface in a relatively short time, the concentrations will most likely be below hazardous levels because of freshwater dilution during the transport process.

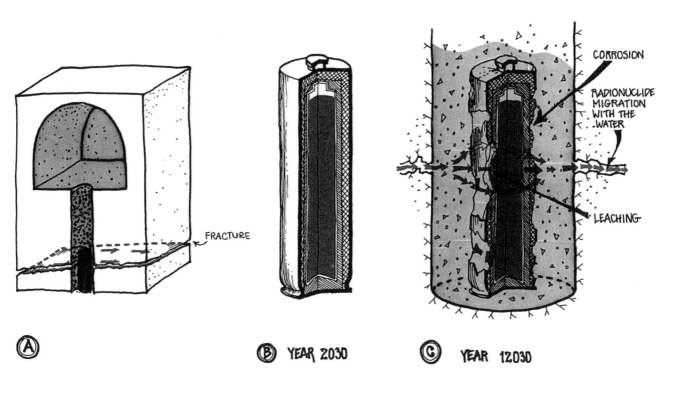

(A)

(B) YEAR 2030

(C) YEAR 12030

FRACTURE

CORROSION

RADIONUCLIDE MIGRATION WITH THE WATER

LEACHING

Disruption of the Repository by Faulting

Faults are fractures in rock where one side of the fracture has moved permanently with respect to the other side. The relative displacement of the two sides can range from a few centimeters to hundreds of kilometers. What would happen to the nuclear wastes in a repository if they were suddenly disturbed by an unexpected fault of major size? This is the question that we shall now address for reprocessing wastes buried in a hard rock repository.

Fig. A. During an ice age the ground surface above a repository will be forced downward by the weight of the ice. The glaciers will erode the surface, and "carve" valleys over zones of weakness in the rock mass. Between ice ages, the ground surface will rise, or "rebound" like a coil spring. During this time, the large zones of weakness will allow adjacent blocks of relatively solid rock to move relative to each other without much resistance. Because the blocks can adjust to each other's movements, it is highly improbable that forces will build up within the blocks and cause large-scale fracturing or faulting. It is for this reason that a repository could be located in a large block of rock which is surrounded by highly fractured zones of weakness.

Fig. B. Regardless of the above reasoning, let us assume that forces do build up in the block and result in a fault formed through the middle of the repository. The new system of fractures in the fault zone will short circuit the contact between the deep flowing groundwater and the water system near the surface. For this highly hypothetical event, let us suppose that 40 canisters of reprocessing waste are severely damaged when the fault is created. It may be assumed further that the glass matrix is crushed into pieces with volumes of 1 cm^3 (about 0.06 in^3) each. From the 40 canisters there will be about 2500 m^2 (27,000 ft^2) of glass surface exposed to the intense groundwater flow in the fault zone. Approximately one deciliter of glass will be leached, or dissolved, into the groundwater each year. This contamination level of the leached glass is equivalent to about 20 g of reprocessing waste (less than one-tenth of an ounce). The danger from this amount of contamination depends on the amount of water flowing through the fault zone and on the amount of water available at the surface for dilution. To maintain the quality required for drinking water, not more than 1 g of reprocessing waste can be mixed with 3.5 million m^3 of water. For dilution of the leached glass from the 40 canisters, 70 million m^3 (billion gal) of fresh water would be required annually. For the present climatic conditions in Sweden, this amount of water would mean an infiltration area of 100 km^2. Infiltration areas of at least this size are not uncommon in Sweden.

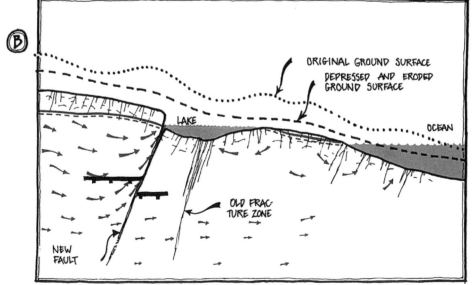

ORIGINAL GROUND SURFACE

DEPRESSED AND ERODED GROUND SURFACE

LAKE

OCEAN

OLD FRACTURE ZONE

NEW FAULT

Disruption of the Repository by Other Natural Events and Human Intrusion

There are other events which could disrupt the repository and increase the probability for hazardous contamination of our water supply by radionuclides. These include earthquakes, meteorite impact, and human intrusion by drilling and/or tunneling.

Fig. A. Frequent earthquakes of relatively high intensity occur mostly in deep zones of weakness in the earth's crust. Stable areas located in the shield between weak zones, and deep sedimentary formations, are relatively free from earthquakes of any substantial intensity. The frequency of earthquakes in these areas is usually quite low.

Fig. B. If a large meteorite should impact the ground surface above a deep repository, the destructive effects should not extend more than about 200 m (650 ft) into the underlying rock formations.

The intact protective cover of protective rock over the repository would, of course, be partly removed.

Fig. C. Drilling and tunneling into the repository by mankind could produce the greatest dangers for human exposure to the radionuclides from the buried nuclear wastes. Exploratory drilling in the rock mass could be for the purposes of locating water supplies, mineral deposits, and geothermal sources. In the future, the use of underground rooms for storage purposes will become more popular. This will increase the exploration efforts, but also improve exploration and construction techniques. It is conceivable that over the next 50 or 60 years these activities will bring substantial advancements in remote explorations technology.

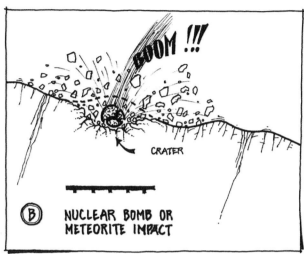

BOOM !!!

CRATER

(B) NUCLEAR BOMB OR
METEORITE IMPACT

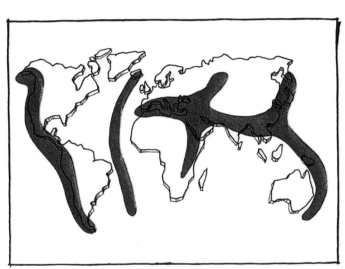

(A) EARTHQUAKE ZONES OF THE WORLD

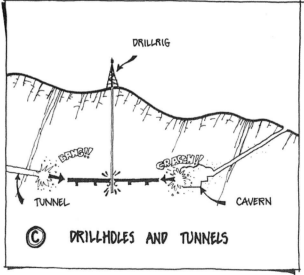

DRILLRIG

BANG!!

CRASH!!

TUNNEL

CAVERN

(C) DRILLHOLES AND TUNNELS

55

What Does it All Mean?

Can We Rely on Bedrock?

Nuclear power plants produce electricity and heat, which are useful forms of energy to mankind. The problem is what to do with the spent fuel, or nuclear waste, during future decades. All the radionuclides must be disposed of in a manner that will not permit ingestation of dangerous quantities by living organisms. The disposal problem will simply not vanish if all nuclear reactors are shut down.

During the past decade, the United States, Canada, Sweden, and the Federal Republic of Germany, as well as other countries with nuclear power reactors, have developed scientific and technical programs to deal with the problem of nuclear waste disposal. A number of solutions have been proposed. These include ejection into outer space, burial in the sediments underlying deep oceans, and burial in deep rock formations in the earth's crust.

Will the disposal method protect us and our descendants from the harmful effects of the nuclear wastes? The deep rock solution offers many advantages as regards achieving the goal.

If reprocessing of spent fuel is selected, then the reprocessing wastes will be "fixed" into a glass matrix, or perhaps a "synthetic" rock form. If reprocessing of spent fuel is not selected, then the fuel rods must first be separated from their metal jackets and then placed in a thick-walled canister.

The safe disposal of nuclear wastes requires that predictions of the actions of mankind and nature must be made for periods of tens and thousands of years. How is it possible to isolate safely the nuclear wastes from all living organisms for such long periods of time?

The spent fuel is more dangerous (toxic) than, for example, uranium ore in nature for a very long time period, perhaps 10,000 years. However, after only several hundred years, the reprocessing waste is less dangerous than uranium ore.

In a repository for radioactive waste, tunnels, disposal rooms, and shafts to the surface will be excavated by mining techniques. Metal canisters of waste would be placed in drillholes in the floors of the disposal rooms. Some time after all the disposal rooms have been used, the remaining tunnels and shafts to the surface will be filled and sealed.

The loadings of past geologic time have created faults, fractures, and joints, and crushed zones in the hard rock formations on earth. Near the surface, the many fractures and joints permit the surface water to flow into the rock, which acts as a reservoir.

Massive deposits of salt occur in many parts of the world, e.g. down the middle of North America, with others located on the southeastern edge of the Great Lakes and the eastern edge of Canada.

Water in nature is caught in a closed cycle of condensation and evaporation. Groundwater in the earth's crust represents the underground part of the cycle. The amount of water infiltration depends on the number of connected voids, cracks, and fractures in the surface soil and rock. Salt in itself will not hold any groundwater.

In most instances, the shape of the groundwater table will approximately match the general contour of the land surface. In other words, there will be pressure differences in the ground water at a certain elevation of the earth's crust.

The quantity of groundwater flowing through a given

cross-sectional area depends on this pressure difference and the resistance to flow. In large bodies of sedimentary rock containing salt formations, the groundwater flows over, under, or around the salt, but never through it under natural circumstances. Many hard rock masses exhibit sizable zones of fractures in which the major amount of groundwater flow is located. In searching for a repository site, it is important to avoid rock masses with many zones of weakness containing relatively large amounts of water.

Except for some future and unpredictable action by mankind, the only way in which the waste could become harmful to living organisms is by transport of the radio-nuclides to the earth's surface by circulating groundwaters. This, of course, requires that the metal canisters must be first damaged by some action of nature, such as faulting of the rock during an earthquake, or by corrosion from chemical reactions with the circulating groundwater in hard rock or with brine in salt. The corrosion of the metal canisters will most certainly occur, but may require hundreds of years if chemically resistant metals, or buffer materials around the canisters, are used. Once the waste is exposed to the circulating groundwater, or to the brine, it must be dissolved, or chemically leached, into solution with the water. This leaching process is quite time consuming. The natural ability of the rock to absorb radionuclide particles as they migrate is also important. Furthermore, it is necessary to understand the factors which can disturb the natural pattern of the groundwater circulation in the rock. Basically, it is the combined effects of excavation operations and heating of the rock which will disturb the groundwater flow pattern.

The heated water around a repository will have a tendency to move upward through joints and connected pores in the rock mass, and be replaced by cooler water from above

and from the sides. However, the regional pressure differences will most likely cause the groundwater to move faster in the horizontal direction as compared to the vertical flow induced by heat from the waste.

Movements of the continents, future ice ages, and erosion of the surface rock over long time periods may cause additional fracturing in the rock masses. This future disturbance of the natural structure of the rock is important if it should occur in regions where nuclear waste repositories were located.

The best forecast of future geologic events in a region must be based on the observable events during the past. It is highly probable that a large rock mass will remain geologically stable over the next tens of thousands of years if it has been stable for the last millions of years. The efforts for locating possible sites for repositories are concentrating on finding such rock masses. Disturbance of the rock structure by changes of the forces in the earth's crust would appear to have more influence on the groundwater circulation than climatic changes on the surface.

Although the fill material surrounding the waste canister will restrict the flow of groundwater, the outer wall of the canister eventually will become saturated with water. As soon as the water makes contact with the canister, the metal will begin to corrode. Depending upon the amount of water flow, its chemical make-up, and the temperature, the corrosion will eventually eat a path through the metal and come into contact with the waste.

The waste will begin to dissolve, however, quite slowly. Some radioactive particles will be transported through the backfill material to the rock. The groundwater will carry the radionuclides into fractures and joints in the rock around the drillhole. Even in the worst situation, involving an early exposure of the waste form to the circulating groundwater, it appears highly unlikely that any radionuclides could migrate from the repository to the ground surface in less than a few thousands of years. Even if the radionuclides reach the surface in a relatively short time, the concentrations will most likely be below hazardous levels because of freshwater dilution during the transport.

There are, admittedly, events which could disrupt the repository and increase the probability for hazardous contamination of our water supply by radionuclides. These include geologic faulting, earthquakes, and meteorite impact. With a proper site selection the risk of such events should be very small.

It would be unwise for us to suggest that mined geological disposal is the best that mankind can devise. Technical advancements in general over the past 100 years have greatly exceeded the wildest expectations and imaginations of the world's best scientific minds of 1880. Solution of the nuclear waste disposal problem requires the concentrated and coordinated efforts of our most talented people. For both practical and scientific reasons, a reasonable disposal method must be selected now and studied in great detail before actual use. This is the situation with mined geological disposal.

Remember that the first waste container will not be placed for permanent disposal in a rock formation for perhaps 20 years or more. Based on multitudes of technology advancements during the last two decades, one should optimistically expect substantial refinements in nuclear waste disposal technology.

Drilling and tunneling into the repository by mankind could produce the greatest dangers for human exposure to the radionuclides from the buried nuclear wastes. It is, however, conceivable that the next 50 or 60 years will bring substantial advancements in remote explorations technology.